Harriet Beveridge

Turnip-Led Weaning

Outrageous Parenting Advice from a Spoof Nanny

Matador
9 Priory Business Park,
Wistow Road, Kibworth Beauchamp,
Leicestershire. LE8 0RX
Tel: 0116 279 2299
Email: books@troubador.co.uk
Web: www.troubador.co.uk/matador
Twitter: @matadorbooks

ISBN 978 1784625 153

British Library Cataloguing in Publication Data.
A catalogue record for this book is available from the British Library.

Printed and bound by CPI Group (UK) Ltd, Croydon, CR0 4YY
Typeset in 11pt Aldine401 BT Roman by Troubador Publishing Ltd, Leicester, UK

Matador is an imprint of Troubador Publishing Ltd

For Katie

This book is dedicated to anyone who:

- Has stared, wild eyed, at a screaming baby in the wee small hours and felt totally and utterly useless.
- Has panicked because they didn't eat a slice of toast at 7.22 a.m. precisely as the celebrity nanny everyone is currently raving about said you MUST.
- Has wondered if they'll ever feel human again as they pass off a poo stain on their shirt as a chocolate stain in the supermarket checkout queue.
- Has felt the world is against them as the umpteenth passer-by gives them 'the look' as their pre-schooler careers around the pavement like a gibbon on caffeine.
- NB: This book is a **spoof**. Please do **not** follow Angelica's ludicrous advice or believe her outrageous views. This is a work of utter fiction not fact.

Contents

Introduction

My name is Angelica Fustain and I am over the moon that you've picked up this book. Are you:

- A parent?
- A parent-to-be?
- Someone who dislikes children, but for regrettable economic reasons has a job which entails spending significant amounts of time with them?

Then this book is for you. I have packed it full of advice about how to handle babies and preschoolers. Other books spout nonsense about which scented candle to use during the birth or which pram-ercise class will flatten your stomach most quickly, but I focus on the truly important things, such as:

- How to implement a suitably complicated bedtime routine for baby so you won't venture out of the house with a noisy child after 4 p.m.

- When's the right time to introduce your child to starched table linen and thereby avoid moral flabbiness later.
- What happens to your ranking in society when you fail to achieve a natural birth.

You may have seen unpleasant comments in the press about me. It is distressing that successful people in Britain receive such jealousy-fuelled negativity. I have to tell myself stoically that it a small price to pay to live in a wonderful country with a thriving monarchy, beautiful countryside and such excellent cheese.

Journalists argue that I cannot dispense sensible advice because I am not a mother myself. What nonsense! It is *because* I do not have children that I maintain a sense of perspective. I have seen too many of my friends suffer the relentless slide into melamine tableware, elasticated trousers and child-centred madness. This book is my attempt to protect society at large from the terrible effects of poor parenting.

For example, have you ever been on a flight where other passengers brought their children? Didn't you witness grown adults humiliate themselves by asking the pilot to sing 'Twinkle twinkle little star' over the tannoy to get their child to sleep? Or have you ever seen a parent in a supermarket lay a Hansel and Gretel style trail of sherbet dib dab to coax their screaming toddler from the checkout to the car? All the while those without children are calmly going about their business with cheerfulness and decorum. I rest my case.

Another criticism levelled at me is that I have no childcare qualifications. It's true that I haven't sat in a classroom and written notes in a neat lever-arch file about childcare theory. *But*, what I have done is spent countless hours with friends and their children, I frequent many baby-friendly cafes and I am a model godmother to William and Zachary. Sadly they have now emigrated to New Zealand, but I have *always* sent them a birthday or Christmas present.

In short I have devoted my life to making the world a better place – a place where you can:

- Go to the supermarket without witnessing a toddler tantrum.
- Ride on a bus without being overcome with the smell of baby sick.
- Enjoy a cappuccino in a café without having a mid-feed naked breast being waved at you unnecessarily.

Join me in my crusade! Read this book, spread the word and together we can make this dream a reality.

In addition to this book I have also developed a host of products to help you – from my breastfeeding winch to my laminated cards on turnip-led weaning, to my nappies with images of inspiring historical figures. I recommend these where pertinent in each chapter. It is so sad that critics claim I am 'cashing in' on my celebrity, and heartbreaking that the Health and Safety Executive are yet to see the merits in so many of my suggestions. I know you understand that I simply have the interests of society, of you and your child at heart. All donations to my legal fighting fund are very gratefully received.

CHAPTER ONE

SLEEPING

The most important thing about night time sleep is that you put the neighbours first. They had no say in your lifestyle choice of becoming a parent, so it's your moral duty to invest in adequate sound proofing to mitigate the risk that you interfere with their quiet bedtime reading.

The next thing to worry about is your husband. It's crucial that the Alpha male is able to go into work boasting that baby is sleeping through the night. If you've actually been up five times in the night to see to baby, then allow yourself a little smile. You are helping to drive economic growth and benefit society, plus hubby might hang around long enough to pay to have your saggy bits fixed.

So how do you ensure your neighbours and your better half gets the peace and quiet they need?

Firstly make sure you have basic soundproofing in place:

- WD40 all doors and bedsprings.

- Replace all creaking cheap floorboards with handmade mahogany ones.
- Throw away any nylon items of clothing which might crackle unexpectedly.

It is unlikely that you'll share a bedroom with your husband in years to come, so why not bite the bullet now and move yourself onto the landing? This has multiple advantages – you are more likely to hear your baby and the hard floor enables you to spring up like a gazelle to go and see to your child.

Once you are absolutely sure your husband is ok, you can turn your attention to baby. The key to a peacefully sleeping baby is the configuration of their bedroom. If you don't have triple glazing, air conditioning and silk bedding then ask yourself if you're really cut out to be a parent – the basics are crucial.

Beyond what is dictated by your bedtime routine (see below) there is absolutely no need for anything else in baby's bedroom. All too often I see cutsie wallpaper, twee pictures and photographs. Baby needs to learn that their room is for sleeping only. Aim for total sensory deprivation. The level of darkness required goes beyond mere black out blinds. Make sure you place black out tape round the door and ceiling rose. You may even need to re-plaster the walls to ensure no light permeates through the bricks.

Babies play up when they want attention from their mother, so invest in a good pair of night vision goggles so you can enter the room in the middle of the night and maintain complete lack of interaction with your child, whilst meeting their basic health requirements. I also recommend a Special Forces – style jumpsuit and helmet. This eliminates all possible signs of your scent when you go to tend to baby.

Mothers often report to me that they struggle with the effects of sleep deprivation in the early months. My previous advice was to have a stomach bypass operation so that you could give yourself coffee enemas whilst ensuring no caffeine entered your breast milk. Sadly those Health and Safety killjoys at the Royal College of Surgeons have firm ideas about the health of the child and the mother, so I am now legally obliged to withdraw this advice. Any donations to the Angelica Fustain legal fighting fund are gratefully received.

If your baby wakes in the night after they are twelve weeks old you have obviously failed. Think carefully about what you have done wrong:

- Is the oxygen content of the room optimal?
- Is there sufficient anchovy paste on baby's swaddling (see the chapter on clothing)?
- Is the room temperature *consistently* at 17.35 degrees? (There's often a dip between 3.45 and 4 a.m. It is well worth ensuring you are awake during this time to check the temperature, as it can have a knock on effect later on in the night.

Go beyond the obvious. You'll read in other books that babies wake again at about 4 or 5 months because they are hungry, but it's actually because by this stage babies have developed sufficient mental alertness to panic when they recognise they are having a disadvantaged start in life.

- Does baby sense you are stupid? Perhaps you should retake your exams to achieve a more robust academic record.
- Does baby feel stressed by your narrow horizons? Are you reading at least one classic work of literature a week? Are you ensuring that your everyday vocabulary with your baby is adequately varied?
- Is the house you are in *really* big enough, or is baby feeling claustrophobic if you have fewer than four floors?

The root of the problem is all too often the bedtime routine. Many parents create complex and time-consuming rituals involving baths, bedtime stories and music and sacrifice a far bigger priority – cooking their husband a decent three course meal. The stability of your relationship is vital to the success of the family unit, so make sure you keep up the basics like starched napkins, floral centrepieces and polished silverware. Many a single mother has rued the day she opted for a ready meal instead of a sensible soufflé with mixed crudities.

With a dash of common sense you can *combine* the complex bedtime rituals with making the supper, by using my handy bedtime step by step guide:

1. COMMUNICATE

Three hours before bedtime gently start giving unconscious signals to your baby that bedtime is round the corner. Why not take up appliquéd patchwork quilt making? Baby will recognise the bedroom-themed activity and start to wind down for the day. It's also such a lovely idea to record your baby's day by day progress through the medium of needlecraft. I saw a stunning example just the other day where a mother had embroidered a scene from each day of their child's first year of life. In glorious multi-coloured silks you could see their first trip to a museum, their first theatre visit and their first ice-skating trip. Quite enchanting.

2. PREPARE YOUR HUSBAND'S MEAL

Start the food preparation – e.g. putting the duck in the marinade or fine slicing the potatoes for a dauphinois. Far too many parents think they have to plonk their child in front of the television to achieve this, thereby missing out on a fabulous opportunity to teach their baby the difference between a Chinese gooseberry and a kumquat. Why not go that extra mile and also use food preparation time to learn another language? You can joyfully explore together what the Chinese might actually call a Chinese gooseberry – oh how droll!

This isn't just immense fun; it's also the chance to

start your child on the straight and narrow path of being a contributing member of society with the potential to resurrect our manufacturing industry by partnering with the emerging Chinese superpower. You may call me a dreamer, but I passionately believe that good parenting is the key to resurrecting the British economy. Check out my website for this week's current deals on my unique Angelica Fustain™ range of international cooking language flash cards. At the time of writing you can buy Chinese for just £44.99 and get Korean half price.

3. CREATE AN ELABORATE PRE-BEDTIME ROUTINE

Why is a complex routine so crucial? The best metaphor I can give you is putting your alarm clock on the other side of the room because it means you will have to physically get up in order to turn it off – the snooze button isn't an option. In a similar vein a complex bedtime routine will remove any temptation to leave baby and have a night away by yourself, because you and only you will be able to execute the elaborate dance of nightlights, snugglies, mobiles and books that gets baby to sleep. What handier way to make sure that hubby doesn't have to get involved and can focus on the Times crossword and consistent trips to the gym? Many a mother has complained to me that they feel stir crazy after a few months and 'need to get away'. Did the 1960s housewife skip off for a spa weekend? No. They focused on needlecraft and cooking to regain their composure.

The complex bedtime routine will also prevent you taking baby away with you to stay with friends, relatives or worse still to a holiday hotel. Such expeditions are simply not fair on others. When friends say they would love to see your child they really mean in a picture or a video on Facebook, they do not mean at 5 a.m. on the landing outside their bedroom when junior will doubtless be screaming and smelling of poo.

In summary, I am less concerned with the *content* of the pre-bedtime routine, but absolutely clear that it needs to be elaborate. Ideas include:

- A bath with mood music and lighting.
- A special game that needs to be played in exactly the right way.
- Different pyjamas for different days of the week.
- A special song for each step of the stairs up to their room
- A homemade book that you have co-created that day, with colour photos of your child's exploits.
- A mobile that needs to hand-wound, or an organic one that biodegrades and needs replacing every few days.

4. PUT YOUR CHILD TO BED

When it comes to the point where you actually put your child into their cot, help them to develop vital independence and a healthy respect for their father's importance as head of the family by popping back to the kitchen immediately to stir your apricot jus or slice your organic chorizo. This is a wonderful way of implementing what other books call 'controlled crying', but in such a more positive, sensible way. As you leave baby's bedroom just say quietly, but firmly "I need to sauté the carrots darling, so go to sleep now." You may find that the first time you try this approach you need to come back to reassure baby a few times. Just be consistent, loving and firm, "I'm liquidizing the gazpacho, time for sleepy sleep sleeps" …"I'm laying the table darling, night night…"

Some mothers have also found it helpful to use visual cues such as bringing a steaming pan into the bedroom so that baby begins to see the logic of your approach – but either way I guarantee that within three nights baby's eyelids will be drooping at the 's' of 'sauté', giving you plenty of time to freshen up before your husband comes back from his demanding day in front of a computer.

Another top tip is to ensure your child has a unique, special toy in their cot. This helps your child to understand that even though mummy is popping back and forth to the kitchen, there will always be a furry, inanimate object that has the comforting smell of your child's own tears and loves them deeply. Ideally choose a soft toy that is just about to go out of production, so it is extra special. You can make friends for life if ever you lose it and have to post desperate pleas on eBay for anyone who can source a Miffy wearing special edition Prince William and Kate commemoration wedding outfit from April 2011 (not the second run with the pink bow, but the original run in cerise). There will be other mothers in the same boat and you can create such a special bond as you go through a time of trauma together.

Early Waking

The last sleeping issue that mothers sometimes come to me with is early wakers – children who start the day at 5 a.m. or even earlier. "By the time we get to 9 a.m. I feel I've had a whole day already, when my husband is just starting his!" lamented one mother. My advice on this issue is: man up! Margaret Thatcher rose early, medieval nuns prayed at Lauds at 5 a.m. and Prime at 6 a.m., Justin Webb must be in a chauffeured car on his way to the Today studio while you are still snoozing. Need I go on? Modern society is fixated on the snooze button – I believe it is a metaphor for our increasingly lazy culture where people are simply unmotivated to find work or follow discipline. You must learn to focus on the positives. What a fantastic opportunity to get into astronomy or to slow cook beef ribs for your husband's dinner, or to write a novel… Be thankful for the blessing of a longer waking day to exercise your talents and contribute to mankind.

Conclusion

If you follow the advice in this chapter there is no reason you can't have a happily sleeping family by the time baby is three months old. It really is a subject I'm passionate about. When I get the bus in the morning, I see so many care-worn, exhausted mothers and it really sets my day off on a bad footing. I bear it patiently, but I do resent the fact that other people's incompetence reduces my ability to complete my Sudoku cheerfully. Getting enough sleep not only helps those around you, but it can make you feel better too. Isn't it wonderful to be useful and to treat yourself at the same time?! As this chapter demonstrates, just a little bit of effort can reap wonderful results.

CHAPTER TWO

BREASTFEEDING

Every mother has to grapple with that challenging time before their child can eat proper food with a knife and fork. I know it is distasteful and disturbing, but the period when your baby needs milk is a time to be endured quietly and patiently. Know that you *will* come through this. More importantly, if you follow my advice you will not only come through this but be able to bask in the knowledge that you did it without disturbing your local community – unlike some women:

I was minding my own business at London Paddington Station the other day, when I found myself surrounded by approximately fifty women breastfeeding. They were brazenly topless – no sign of an Angelica Fustain™ breastfeeding kaftan in sight. A fellow traveler explained to me that it was a 'flash mob', campaigning for women's rights to breastfeeding in public. Well I'm sorry but I don't think Emily Davison threw herself under the King's

Horse in order to allow women to antagonize innocent bystanders by exposing their stretch marks.

If you really must breastfeed then do it *discreetly*. I am strongly convinced that the Credit Crunch and ensuing Eurozone Crisis was mainly to blame on the younger generation eating snacks whilst not sitting down, wearing denim everyday and seeing breastfeeding at the local library. Is it any wonder that they grew up confusing work and leisure, public and private and believing that anything goes?

There are a few simple steps to discreet breastfeeding:

1. LOCATION

Do it at home, in a room designated specifically for the purpose. I find a utility room works best. This has a multitude of advantages:

- It is out of the way so feeding won't interfere with your husband watching the Rugby Highlights.
- The sound of the washing machine will mask any distasteful slurping noises.
- It allows you to multitask and do a spot of ironing or cashmere hand-washing while junior is busy.

2. TIMING

Think carefully about what times will best suit your husband. Night time feeding can be a wonderful way of giving baby calories without impacting on your husband's routine – just remember to do it quietly. Once your baby sleeps through the night they may be peckish first thing in the morning. The utility room is the ideal room to feed them whilst popping in and out of the kitchen to cook a full English breakfast for your husband.

3. Planning for Emergencies

I do appreciate that in the Real World you may have to leave the house at an inconvenient time in order to visit the delicatessen for those fresh, seasonal dinner party ingredients that are so essential to a properly functioning marriage. When this happens simply follow these tips to ensure that public breastfeeding is as unobtrusive to your fellow members of society as possible:

4. Clothing

Make sure you are completely covered up. Your child's mouth is no bigger than a walnut, so there is absolutely no need to expose your full bosom, your stomach, your shoulders or, God forbid, all of the above. My Angelica Fustain™ range of fashionable kaftans has an ingenious wrap-around design that will fully cover you and baby. In fact I've heard numerous stories from delighted customers of having lunch with friends and their friends being totally unaware that they had their baby with them, let alone that they were breastfeeding them. How wonderful!

5. POSITIONING

It is during latch on that there is the greatest risk of aureole exposure. Countless times I've seen innocent men become hypnotically entranced by the circular waving of a mammary as a mother incompetently waves her double Ds in front of an infant's mouth. One minute a man is sipping a cappuccino in their favourite eatery, taking a well-earned break from oiling the wheels of corporate success and the next he is confronted with a semi-naked banshee accusing him of ogling her chest.

Who is really at fault here? Any self-respecting mother simply needs to carry a spirit level and a portable winch. Once babies are tipped at 38 degrees, latch on is practically automatic. My Angelica Fustain™ baby winch comes in a choice of shades (mauve or terracotta), can be attached to any good quality coffee table and the luxury version even has a remote controlled winch action, all for just £149.99.

BOTTLE FEEDING

I am a big supporter of bottle feeding. I know that by saying this I put myself in grave personal danger. There are dark rumours on internet chat rooms that the NCT has sleeping cells of heavily armed anti-bottle militia.

I must confess to a few sleepless nights worrying how they will react to this book. My publishers may well sneer that this is a lunatic conspiracy theory, but I respect the views of username 'Grassyknoll' on Mumsnet. I just hope my publishers can look at themselves in the mirror of a morning, knowing they turned down my highly reasonable request for body guards and a Pope Mobil on my upcoming book tour.

Despite the personal danger it puts me in I do feel it is my duty to give you an honest, calm assessment of the pros and cons of bottle-feeding, free from the bias and hysteria one so often encounters in this debate.

THE DISADVANTAGES OF BREASTFEEDING:

Breastfeeding makes other people extremely uncomfortable. It is hard to maintain conversation when one can only look someone directly in the eye and nowhere else. For example, I once lunched with a friend when she was breast feeding and this meant I was absolutely unable to glance down at my meal for fear of getting a voyeuristic glimpse of nipple. As a result I ate a bit of onion in my salad nicoise directly after a slice of egg, thereby entirely missing out on the complex layered flavours of onion/ French bean/egg/seared Bluefin tuna which is so central to the salad nicoise experience.

THE ADVANTAGES OF BOTTLE FEEDING

Just think of the number of people bottle feeding keeps in employment: the factory workers who manufacture the bottles, the lab technicians who develop the formula, the breeders of the rats it has been tested on, the sales assistants in the airport shops who sell it to you after you've gone through security to foil jihadist toddlers... All rendered unemployed and useless all because of the thoughtlessness of breast feeding mothers who have the cheek to call their selfish behaviour 'natural'. I daresay it may not be 'natural' to defecate in lavatories or use Farrow and Ball paint, but I don't see mothers quibbling on these topics, do you?!

Bottle feeding also makes it more difficult to shift your baby weight. I've heard that breastfeeding makes the weight simply fall away, where is the personal developmental learning experience there? It's also simply not fair on those of us who have chosen not to have children. We have spent the hours in the gym and resisted the temptation of that extra biscuit at the local history society lecture, so why should you have it easy? It is far more respectful to society to work hard to shed the extra pounds, and what a marvellous way of reminding you to make the most of your appearance. I've noticed that many new mothers de-prioritise make up and hair-styling and own more baby-sick muslins than decent silk headscarves.

Hopefully a battle against extra weight will help you snap out of it and reacquaint yourself with lip gloss.

CONCLUSION

I trust my reasoned, impartial advice strikes home. Breastfeed if you must, but bottle-feeding is so much easier and less stressful for everyone else. I leave you with this salutatory tale: only just today I was waiting for the bus and saw a mother attempting to breastfeed her child in the bus queue. This meant I felt obliged to offer her my seat in the shelter – when I quite obviously had some new court shoes that were chaffing uncomfortably – and meant our boarding of the bus was delayed by a number of seconds as she fiddled provocatively with a bra strap so vast it rivaled the suspension cables on the Forth Road Bridge. Our driver seemed most distracted for the rest of the trip – I can't believe that breastfeeding promotes road safety.

CHAPTER THREE

CRYING

Babies are 70% lungs and 30% bottom my mother used to joke. She is wrong on countless topics (including when it's appropriate to move to a care home rather than drop heavy hints to her daughter about a granny flat), but she is right on that score. Babies have lungs and when babies cry they can split rocks with their wailing. But just because they *can* does not mean they *should*. Have you ever been to a wedding which has been ruined by a baby crying? It's the most profound journey in a woman's life: walking up the aisle in the most expensive dress she will ever possess, getting everyone's attention no matter how plain she is, looking towards the man who will complete her existence…

When 'waaaaaaaaaaaaaaaaaaaaaaaaaaaaa' … a selfish mother allows her baby to destroy the moment. The mother then gives an apologetic look as she stumbles out of the pew, the crying ricocheting off the church pillars as she noisily exits, swinging the 14th century oak door behind her. While the poor bride tries valiantly to fall back in step with the trumpet voluntary, the friends of the offending mother and baby ignore her as they are too busy shrugging their shoulders ruefully as if to say, 'don't worry, these things happen.' Shame on you collaborators! The bride has spent eighteen months planning how the floristry should complement the guests' fascinators and this is how she is rewarded! A crying child is simply a sign of terrible parenting and should not be tolerated.

Crying babies are not merely distressing for those in earshot, they also weaken the state of our country. I took the trouble of doing some statistical analysis, exploring the correlation between crying in public, and the prevalence of wars or economic malaise. Can it be co-incidence that footballer Paul Gasgoine cried in 1990 and then we had a recession and a Gulf war? Or that people openly wept about the death of Princess Diana in 1997 and in the same year there was an Asian economic crisis? Public displays of weeping are simply not good for global confidence, prosperity and international peace. I believe the rot starts early and that our increasing leniency on babies crying is storing up horrific problems for the future of the world. Sadly the article I submitted to the Daily Mail on this topic was returned, unpublished. I think it sad that they lacked the moral fibre to say what needs to be said.

For those failing parents whose children *do* cry, I'll spend the rest of this chapter helping you make less of the disaster:

Step one – prevent your child from crying in the first place

Prevention is better than cure. Here are the top ten things you can do to stop your child crying:

1. Invest in an Angelica Fustain™ nanny.
2. Use a dummy at all times, up to the age of eight.
3. Ensure baby is never bored – see the chapter on toys and activities, such as the Angelica Fustain™ portable macramé kit.
4. Ensure baby never goes hungry by carrying baby bottles, milk and a portable microwave at all times.
5. Install inbuilt speakers into your pram to play soothing light opera to keep your child calm.
6. Ensure baby's temperature is always perfect – always use cashmere or alpaca clothing.
7. Employ a children's entertainer to accompany you at all times. When they are not making balloon animals or doing magic tricks they can be terribly useful carrying shopping or parking the car for you – just do make sure they are properly CRB checked.
8. Make sure baby always feels at home. Bring familiar items from home so that even in the virgin territory of a new supermarket or café they still feel safe and nurtured: a favourite cooking pot, a sample of your sitting room carpet or wallpaper for example.
9. It's well documented that movement soothes a child

so invest in an electric pram that creates perpetual motion. The Angelica Fustain™ rock-a-pram is ideal, and highly reasonable at only £899.75. Ignore the scaremongering about this wonderful product which the ever-unreliable 'Which?' Website is bandying about. The 'on' and 'off' switches are very clearly marked and I am challenging their calls to withdraw it on health and safety grounds with the utmost vigour.

10. Never leave the house – then at least no one will hear your child if you do fail as a parent and they cry.

Step two – identify the types of cry and what they mean

If you struggle with the ten, easy preventative steps then sadly disaster may still strike. What do you do if your baby does cry? It is so important that you diagnose thing properly – imagine mistaking a high pitched staccato cry with a medium pitched intermittent cry! The consequences can be devastating. Sadly most mothers simply pick up their babies and cuddle them whenever they cry, which creates the kind of selfish bond that means so many twenty-something adults today still live with their parents. Don't believe the stories in the media about young people not being able to afford their own homes – look carefully at the news footage and you'll see the tell-tale signs – perhaps they are wearing a shirt that mummy ironed or nibbling on a homemade scone – that prove it is softness not hardship that glues them to their childhood home.

Download my 'crying app' for smart phones. It goes through the 50 fundamental types of crying. The app works very simply: hold your crying baby up to the phone and it will diagnose the type of cry in seconds and tell you what to do. If it deems that the cry is not for a legitimate reason it will start to rebuke your child firmly, accompanied by the rousing sound of a military marching band – that usually does the trick. Here I give you a sneak preview of a few of those 50 types of cry:

STACCATO CRY FOLLOWED BY WISTFUL 'HMMMM'

You are breastfeeding and your child is craving a bottle. The staccato cry signifies baby's revulsion at having to go near a cheap nylon nursing bra, coupled with a concern it will get an electric shock from the nylon rubbing on their polyester mix Babygro. The wistful 'hmmm' shows how sad baby is at the thought of the diligent hours spent by scientists perfecting baby formula, versus the unpleasant tang of garlic they can taste in your milk. The taste is not just unpleasant in itself, but also – more worryingly – signifies a slipping of standards because it shows you made a hurried pasta and pesto supper last night. Baby is coming to terms with the knowledge that they might be left fatherless as your slackness causes hubby to leave you for someone who has the gumption to hand baste pheasant and stuff mushrooms.

HIGH PITCHED, DESPERATE

Baby does not like the colour of outfit you have put them in. If you dress your male child in anything other than blue he should undoubtedly cry. If he doesn't he may well grow up to be an interior designer and you should seek immediate medical advice. Please refer to the chapter on clothing to understand more deeply the profound psychological impact of too much fuchsia at a tender age.

POINTED TONGUE, VERY LOUD, BEETROOT FACE

Baby does not condone the company you are keeping or the locations you frequent. If you find it happening in more reputable establishments your child may well be trying to alert you that you are embarrassing yourself in trying to rise above your station. The poor darling is trying to deflect attention from you as you use the wrong knife for the butter. I run some highly practical Angelica Fustain™ 'deportment and manners' workshops, which I strongly recommend you attend. They do only run in Tuscany in May, but I think it's so vital that people show commitment when they sign up for education that I think this is a fair test of potential participants' resolve. Please note that regretfully we are unable to accommodate children at this location.

UNDULATING, MOURNFUL WAIL

Baby has lost something – this might be something tangible like a toy, or something more fundamental, like a feeling of respect for its parents. The Angelica Fustain™ 'emotional distress identification cards' are a fantastic way of dealing with this type of cry. In cheerful laminated plastic, this easy-to-wipe deck of cards show a huge variety of pictures of distressing events – from a teddy bear falling down a drain right through to a warzone. Even very young babies are able to point to or indicate with their eye movements the picture that most closely resembles the incident they are distressed about. Once you've identified the issue, simply turn over the card to reveal the suggestion about how to tackle the emotional distress.

For example, on the back of the 'lost teddy' card is the recommendation to visit local tip to show your child what really happens to all material items. So many parents dress up the realities of the world and children become soft skinned and less able to cope with challenges later. It is far better to teach them to man up and prepare for a life that can be harsh and unfair than to sugar coat things for them. I am well aware that an Internet Troll has reviewed this card pack on Amazon as "twisted, dark and corrosive" and had the gall to suggest that being 'jilted at the altar' has warped my view of the world. On the contrary, Anthony and I came to a happy, mutual decision about the break off of our engagement and I know he was as surprised and delighted as I was when he found himself in love with my best friend and announced his engagement a couple of weeks later. It is a testament to the miracles of modern medicine that their baby boy arrived 7 months later looking and behaving like a full-term baby.

CRYING ACCOMPANIED BY BLOOD, VOMITING, OR A RASH

There is always the chance that your child is actually unwell. It is my duty to advise you to call NHS Direct and then go to your GP and then progress to A&E. It's saddening that so many mothers ignore NHS Direct and go straight to the Doctor's surgery. Those of us with persistent, painful migraines can well do without babies' piercing cries in the waiting room. We are doing important work, pressing on despite pharmaceutical propaganda and the medical Establishment's lies that we must give up alcohol, chocolate and coffee as 'basic requirements' before we'll be 'considered' for prescription morphine or Reiki.

WHEN CRYING IS ACCEPTABLE

There are a few, exceptional circumstances when crying is acceptable:

FREQUENT AND PERSISTENT CRYING

In a handful of cases, this can be an indication of early theatrical promise. Turn one of the rooms in your house into a miniature replica of the Globe Theatre. Whenever your baby cries simply put them in there, play a suitable recording of Romeo and Juliet or The Cherry Orchard and look forward to the BAFTA acceptance speeches in years to come. Do be sure to choose the recordings and scenery carefully – sloppy use of props will mean Junior ends up as a walk-on in the Bill or an incest sub-plot in EastEnders. Do you really want to be on celebrity Family Fortunes in 20 years' time? Praying that Mrs Smythe next door isn't watching and knowing in your heart of hearts that she does but will be too ashamed to admit she tunes into ITV and a hideous awkwardness of I know-that-you-know-that-I-know type conversations will ensue

    …but I digress.

HALF-HEARTED, INTERMITTENT

This is the mark of a highly intelligent child already confronting the fundamental ennui of man's quest for meaning and purpose in a post-modernist world. If you have employed a children's entertainer, as advised above, you might want to reconsider and employ a Zen Master or Philosophy Tutor. At the very least make sure you intersperse the Peppa Pig cardboard books so ubiquitous in prams today with a Nietzsche picture book or two. It is almost certain that you child will go on to take one of two paths:

1.   Become a Nobel Prize Winner or Poet Laureate.
2.   Become a park-bench-dwelling methadone abuser.

It can be overwhelming for some parents to realise that they and they alone can make the difference between happiness and misery, success and failure – indeed not just of their child but the wider human race. Enrol in an Angelica Fustain™ parenting class NOW.

Conclusion

I trust that has been a useful exploration into the highs and lows of crying. I will leave you with this story, which I hope encapsulates all that you've learned from this chapter:

I was in the queue at the greengrocers recently – experiencing a frisson of fear that someone ahead of me would nab the last remaining aubergine and ruin my evening Moussaka plans – when a woman came in with a crying baby. There were lots of sympathetic clucks from the lady at the head of the queue and much exhausted eye rolling and ineffectual 'there there's' from the mother to her baby. Imagine my horror when the cry (quite clearly a staccato cry followed by wistful 'hmmmm', indicating a breastfed child craving a bottle) crescendoed to such a point that the lady at the head of the queue *offered the mother to jump the queue and be served next.* Well I could see the aubergine as good as pureed into weaning cubes before my very eyes!

Quick as a flash I brought out the bottle and ready-made infant milk sachet I carry with me at all times, as I believe all upstanding citizens should, and said clearly and calmly to the baby:

"It's alright, your mother simply doesn't know any better, help is at hand," and wordlessly pressed the gifts into the parent's hands. The mother, doubtless overcome with relief, burst into grateful tears and fled the shop immediately – I hope to feed the poor infant as it really was bellowing by now. My fellow shoppers, with looks of horror at how inadequate they felt in the face of such calm competence, indicated silently that I should jump the queue. Needless to say, buoyed up with the knowledge that I had, yet again, helped people so dramatically, I went on that evening to cook the most delicious moussaka I have ever created.

CHAPTER FOUR

CHANGING

Why does the word 'poo' make so many people giggle? I don't understand it. It's a natural, essential part of everyone's life and yet it makes even the most sane and sensible people dissolve into fits. I have perfected an exercise to help people face up to poo and deal with it calmly. Get a pencil and paper and write down every single word for poo or going for a poo you can think of. As an example, here's one from a middle class mother of three I befriended in a baby café in Chiswick (she came in expecting a cappuccino and after a chance encounter with me came out a changed woman):

- Poo, biggies, effluent, faeces, excreta, bottom baggage, Mr Tim's, twosies, room-clearer,
- Off to fill the potty, do the business, sprinkle some fertilizer, lighten the load, scare the neighbours, kill the moths, embarrass the dog, start divorce proceedings

There, is it all out now? Feeling better? Then let us calmly proceed.

What goes in must come out, but the majority of mothers mismanage this simple task, with profound consequences on the rest of us innocent bystanders. It's just not on. Smoking is now banned in public places – you see the poor addicted souls hunched up in all weathers outside buildings – so why is infant anal effluent vapor tolerated? In this chapter I will guide you on a number of vital topics.

1. How to anticipate your child's bowel movements.
2. Whether to choose disposable nappies or washable ones.
3. How to spot a full nappy before anyone else does.
4. How to exit a conversation gracefully in order to deal with a full nappy with minimum fuss.
5. Nappy disposal protocols for sensible citizens.
6. How to deal with the smell.

1. How to Anticipate Your Child's Bowel Movements

Babies give very obvious warning clues – a slight widening of the eyes or a wave of the hand – to show they are about to perform. If you are missing your baby's cues it's probably because you aren't paying them enough attention. If you are changing more than three dirty nappies in a day then take this as valuable feedback on your overall parenting competence.

It is never too early to potty train. At the very latest you should be sitting your child on a potty from three months immediately after breakfast, lunch and before bath time. Your child will soon learn that these are the appropriate times and location to defecate. Reward them for their efforts – this time on the potty is a wonderful opportunity to spend quality time with your child. Read them inspiring poetry and political tracts, show them great works of art and literature. My Angelica Fustain™ leather-bound anthology 'Carpe Diem on the potty' is ideal for this and a snip at only £49.99.

I do appreciate that there are some practical challenges to sitting your baby on the potty if they are on the less advanced end of the developmental curve and therefore unable to sit independently at three months old. No matter! The current design of potties is the result of a carefully coordinated conspiracy by the disposable nappy manufacturers, so that you have to use their products for a number of years before your baby is able to progress to a potty. What nonsense! My Angelica Fustain™ potties have a unique set of body splints and tying mechanisms so that you can secure even a very young baby to the potty when they are just a few weeks old. The product is patent pending, but I am quietly confident that we will resolve the underarm chaffing issues which have been reported in the Press very quickly indeed.

I am, however, a realist and I realise that for many parents it may be a full six to nine months before I can reasonably expect you to have potty training mastered. So what to do in the meantime? The big debate centres on whether to use disposable or washable nappies. Let me guide you on this crucial area:

2. DISPOSABLE OR WASHABLE NAPPIES?

In the last couple of decades disposable nappies have become the norm. In the UK alone there are approximately 2.8 billion of them being dumped in landfill *per year.* Now some critics have used the fact that there is a proposed new landfill site half a mile from my gorgeous holiday cottage to launch shallow accusations of my bias on this topic. Balderdash! It is true that I believe there is no place for domestic waste in Upper Didsbury-Compton. I strongly believe landfill sites should be positioned near housing estates. This is not NIMBYISM, just a common sense way to ensure low-cost housing for the young and the poor.

But I digress…!

The thing that really troubles me about disposable nappies is the proliferation of cutsie cartoon pictures on them. Do we really have to have the likes of Pooh Bear and Lightening McQueen associated with our everyday bodily functions? I believe these images are creating unconscious bias amongst youngsters, parents – indeed anyone who watches television and chances upon an advert for nappies (and I encountered one whilst innocently watching a truly riveting programme on recent archaeological finds in Suffolk).

Pooh Bear associated with poo, I get the joke and no it's *not* funny, it's just puerile. No wonder we are seeing such a dumbing down of cultural standards. Lightening McQueen and poo? What a depressing first step in the relentless Americanisation of our children that ends up with teenagers using 'like' as an adverb rather than a verb and wanting to skateboard in inappropriate – quite clearly pedestrianised – areas.

So, I hear you cry, you must be suggesting washable nappies then Angelica? Certainly not! Items that need laundering need drying. The 'ecologically aware' couple living next to me at number one have ruined countless al fresco Book Club meetings at my house by festooning their washing line with innumerable greying rags of terry toweling. Disposable nappies *are* the way forward, we just need to dispose of them in an appropriate fashion (more on that anon…).

I have brought out my own range of disposable nappies complete with inspirational pictures. Only Angelica Fustain™ nappies come with images of Florence Nightingale, Barack Obama and Einstein. By introducing these figures in an everyday context right from the word go we are sending a powerful message to our children that *they too can excel* – despite mediocre parents.

3. How to spot a full nappy before anyone else does

Many mothers think it is perfectly acceptable to sniff their baby's fully clad bottom to check if it needs changing. It's so saddening that we've descended to such awful standards. It's humiliating for the child – one minute they are crawling about learning the difference between real wood and laminate flooring – the next they are hoisted aloft with no warning and sniffed without permission. I am not surprised the youth of today do not respect authority.

I am awaiting patent approval for a unique alarm system that will let you know when danger is imminent. A sensor in the Angelica Fustain™ nappy monitors methane levels and sends a wireless signal to a wristband worn by the mother, and this given the mother an electric shock. Prototypes did trial an audible alarm, but user tests showed this was intensely irritating to bystanders.

4. How to exit a conversation gracefully in order to deal with a full nappy with minimum fuss

Please avoid the unnecessary hullabaloo that one so often sees when a mother is off to change an infant's nappy. There is NO need to draw attention to yourself. I was dedicated enough in my research for this book to spend a number of mornings in the local Marks and Spencer café to capture some real life examples. These included:

- 'Wow! That's a room-clearer, how can something so small s★★t more than its body weight?!'
- 'Phew, we should bottle that and sell it the military, my eyes are watering!'
- 'Alert! Alert! The sewage farm is experiencing a code red, repeat a code red!'

These are *not* funny; they are loud, vulgar proclamations which simply ruin everyone else's macchiatos. Go quickly and go quietly. I do understand that you may need to explain to your companions that you are about to exit the conversation temporarily, but I think 99.9 % of the population will absolutely guess without you having to spell it out to them. They will hardly think you and junior are off to play backgammon (the pieces are really too small for the under ones, thereafter it is admittedly a fabulous way of spending quality time with your child). If there is any chance of misunderstanding then use euphemisms. This is what the British have done with wonderful effect for centuries. We don't use the lavatory in the UK, we 'spend a penny' or 'go to visit the smallest room in the house'. Women don't go into the gory details of feminine hygiene products to explain to their friends why they are missing aqua aerobics: we simply mention that 'the redcoats have arrived or 'Aunt Flo is coming for a visit'.

Make sure your baby changing bag includes the basics:

- Fresh nappies, wipes, airlock disposal bags.
- A complete change of clothing for junior (the vapours have travelled through the clothing, so they must always be changed).
- A housecoat for you to wear whilst conducting the change.
- A complete change of clothing for you for once the change is complete.
- Antibacterial spray, surgical gloves and disposable sheeting.
- A pop up camping table to ensure junior has no contact with 'public' changing areas. They are quite disgusting and I believe are solely responsible for the rise of more virulent strains of E. coli.
- A pop up tent for instant privacy.

5. NAPPY DISPOSAL PROTOCOLS FOR THE SENSIBLE CITIZEN

You must always take a dirty nappy home with you. It is incredibly bad form to leave your used nappy in someone else's bin, be that in a church hall, a public litter bin, or heaven forbid someone else's house. That is akin to the dog walkers who think 'cleaning up after their dog' means putting the excrement into a clear plastic bag and then throwing it into a hedge. When I volunteered for the local residents' canal pathway regeneration project, I was hoping to plant wild primroses, not gather shrink-wrapped faeces. Even worse are those who can't even throw properly and snag the bags on overhead branches, like piñatas of doom, waiting to fall on an innocent walker. I am very sad that our local council seems not to have taken seriously my suggestion of a permanent police presence at 20 yard intervals along all footpaths, and my local MP has not replied to my letter advocating stiff jail sentences for errant dog owners. Go to *www.helpfulhumour.com* now and sign the petition.

But I digress…

The piece de resistance of the Angelica Fustain™ nappy system is… the DIY home grown landfill kit. Simply apply for planning permission for a basement extension, once completed erect my soon-to-be-patented set of air lock doors and hey presto! Your very own landfill site that is local, convenient and has no impact on neighbours and the community. The authorities have provocatively insisted that they would not grant planning permission for this use of a basement extension – indeed they are taking me to court on the trumped up charge of 'inciting law-breaking'. With your generous donations to the Angelica Fustain legal fighting fund I *know* that justice will prevail.

6. HOW TO DEAL WITH THE SMELL

You may think your child smells of freshly cut grass and their excrement is as docile as Weetabix, but the rest of the world do not. It can take hours or even days for a room to be truly cleansed after a single poorly-managed nappy episode. After my nephews came to visit last Christmas I had to cordon-off the sitting room for a week before it felt appropriate to congregate there again. This meant the local Neighbourhood Watch meeting was postponed at terrifying risk to us all.

Think carefully about home fragrance strategies. Why not make every room unique with its own floral note? This will help baby orient themselves and accelerate their spatial awareness. The high achievers amongst you can create indoor gardens – perhaps an Orangery in the bathroom, lavender planters on the stairways and juniper hanging baskets in the kitchen.

The obvious next step to the indoor garden is to distil your own perfume. What a symbol of your successful family unit! What better way to give your little one a sense of belonging and importance! Take it out and about with you to mitigate the olfactory damage you can otherwise create when you stray outside your home. Another side benefit is that this might become a thriving cottage industry for you, as the pressing and bottling can easily be fitted round your child and husband's needs and will be a wonderful learning opportunity for your child. Yes it does take a bit of effort, but imagine how fulfilling it will be in a couple of years when your confident toddler proactively suggests a eucalyptus spritz to their menopausal Nursery Key Worker.

In conclusion

I will leave you with this salutary tale of the devastating effects poor nappy management can have. I hope it spurs you to follow my advice in this chapter to the letter:

I was perusing our delightful local Crabtree and Evelyn outlet the other day when my senses were transfixed by an aroma of lily of the valley and Earl Grey. In an instant I was transported back to when I was seven years old and went to Miss Crosby's house every Tuesday to learn piano. The lily of the valley was the scent she always wore and the Earl Grey was the tea she always sipped as she guided me gently through my scales. The pianoforte has been such a constant source of solace to me in a sometimes challenging solitary life and to be able to remember so vividly the start of my romance with Chopin and Schubert was a joy. Imagine my horror when the moment was shattered by a fellow customer peering into her pram and proclaiming to her friend,

'Lordy! He's sh★t all the way up his back!! Pureed carrot is *off* the menu for you, little Lord Farty-bottom.'

She had the audacity to *finish making her purchase* before exiting the shop. My memories of Miss Crosby were ruined and I can only hope that a few restorative evenings practicing 'Fur Elise' will restore my equanimity.

CHAPTER FIVE

TURNIP-LED WEANING

Just when you've seen sense and got Junior onto formula milk in bottles it's time for another potentially terrifying step – weaning. Never fear, my turnip-led weaning is the answer. Yes – it has been much criticised by so-called 'Nutritionists', but I refuse to take them seriously. All 'Nutritionists' have done is waltz around a university campus for a couple of years, bored people witless about the protein content of bean curd and changed their mind about the value of goji berries. Honestly! Food is just common sense; I don't need some pseudo-scientific 'qualification'.

Let me guide you through why weaning is important, my three weaning principles and then I'll finish the chapter with a comprehensive menu planner and a word on the mealtime environment.

WHY CORRECT WEANING IS CRUCIAL

We are what we eat and those first precious weeks of weaning are when vital neural networks are laid down. It's how you act as a parent *now* which will determine whether your child will appreciate a good Chablis and thrive, or ruin their social prospects by preferring Blue Nun.

I am not encouraging an unseemly scrambling up the social ladder, I will leave it to you to assess your place in the pecking order, I merely want to point out gently the difference between dough balls and 'popcorn chicken', tomato ketchup and brown sauce, fish fingers and goujons of plaice. Let's just say that I very much doubt the Queen is a fan of the kind of pies one can buy at garage forecourts. Don't let your child's eating habits impact the quality of their friendship and marriage prospects.

How successfully you wean your child will also impact their wider ability to accept life's ups and downs with resilience and verve. There is nothing worse than sitting in a café on a Sunday morning, perusing the weekend papers, endeavouring to recharge my batteries after a long week spent helping others, when the tranquillity is shattered as I hear a child exclaim,

'Yuk! I am NOT eating that OLIVE and there is a LETTUCE LEAF on my plate! I am SHOPPING you to Social Services for CHILD CRUELTY!!'

Is there any better example of the self-centred, self-absorption of the young generation? And isn't it terrifying that the current trend is for *baby-led* weaning?! Help me to turn the tide, otherwise we will have millions of children growing up to be selfish enough to... well... for example plant roses which quite blatantly clash with their neighbours' hollyhocks... and yes Mrs Green – my neighbour at number three – I *am* referring to you directly and to hell with your lawyers threatening letters. For your information, Mrs Green, 'slander' is when you defame someone for speaking a lie, but courage on the other hand, courage is when you speak up against horticultural bullies.

...but I digress...

Another obvious impact is how *internationally mobile* your child will be. A baby with a limited palette is much more likely in later life to subconsciously resist an international job posting which could further their career dramatically. As I drive through the dilapidated industrial parks of Slough I get quite choked thinking how different our export prospects might be if only more people sampled noodles from an early age.

The last consequence of weaning we ought to speak about is the impact it has on your child's ongoing health, weight and vigour. As you spoon baby food into your child's mouth are you hastening them towards lifelong health or lifelong elasticated trousers?

The Three Fundamental Weaning Principles

So now we've looked at how important weaning is, let's move on to my three fundamental principles:

Principle one – Use tried and tested diets

Forget modern fads, look at nutritional approaches which are absolutely tried and tested. Consider when and where people were doing well in history and what specifically were they eating when this success happened. Britain in the wartime Blitz instantly springs to mind, America in the 1960s working towards the moon landings, Brazil today... There are countless examples out there of diets and eating habits we can replicate for the advancement of our own children.

In my next book I will be going one stage further and look at the personality traits you want from your child, and the diets of suitable role models. I am currently diligently researching what Margaret Thatcher ate in her formative years and the role that Mandela's diet of stale prison bread played in the dismantling of apartheid. If you are as passionate as I am about this topic you can make a very real difference by contributing to my international travel fund. My publishers are not visionary enough to understand that visiting key international locations such as Buenos Aries and the Maldives is integral to the authenticity of my next book and they are frustratingly sceptical about my devastating lumbago and the impossibility of travelling Economy. Every pound you can donate brings us a step closer to appropriately weaned children across the world.

PRINCIPLE TWO – CONDITION THE PALETTE.

Learn from the tactics of the all-powerful media: the television conditions our youth into believing that Essex is fashionable and 'Urban music' is somehow cooler than Barber Shop Harmony, so get to your child before the advertisers do and *condition* your child into believing that certain foods are 'cool' and others are not.

As an aside, I have written to Waitrose expressing my concern about their use of muted green logo and Heston Blumenthal in terrifying glasses– I believe they are putting off young children and thereby pushing them into the tacky embrace of discount supermarkets. If our children are scared of Waitrose Essentials guacamole I shudder to think about the younger generation's emerging standards of quality and the impact that will inevitably have on the British Manufacturing industry.

But I digress…

My Angelica Fustain™ palette conditioning App is incredibly good value at £15.99. Simply type in a certain food type and the app will display it with a positive or negative association. So for example there are carefully photo-shopped pictures showing a child drinking cod liver oil nestled against his loving mother reading a storybook together. Then there is the picture of a sad child eating a doughnut in a room bereft of toys or colour, except for a teddy bear which shakes its head, says, 'I don't want to play with you any more,' and leaves the scene. I am expanding my range so look out for palette conditioning placemats, aprons and kitchen wallpaper, all coming soon.

If you really are a loving parent you'll appreciate how worthwhile it is to invest in celebrity endorsements. Take for example my efforts to convince Jessica Ennis to sponsor our local campaign for pedestrians to use the pavements safely: to overtake other walkers only when absolutely necessary and when resorting to this emergency measure to do so slowly and calmly. (How many times have you felt a dangerous wind tunnel as people rush by you? It's an accident waiting to happen). Although we haven't quite had confirmation from Jessica yet I am quietly confident that with her help decorum will prevail.

What's the relevance to your baby's weaning? Well time and again I've seen that a fussy eater refusing stewed liver just needs a visit from Mr Tumble or the Wiggles to persuade them cheerfully of the 'coolness' of offal . The Angelica Fustain talent agency has an impressive range of baby-orientated celebrities on our books and each visit only costs £5000 plus VAT and agency commission – it really is a no-brainer for the committed parent.

Principle Three – Use Local, Seasonal Substitutability

With a bit of creative thinking you can promote your child's future international mobility whilst also supporting the local economy today. The key is to think about substitutes, for example does the recipe really *need* a banana, or would a swede do just as well? On recent holidays to Spain it has profoundly saddened me to see field upon field of poly tunnels sheltering tomatoes and strawberries. What a horrific double impact – jobs are being taken away from British Farmers and at the same time space is being taken up in Spain that would be so much better used for holiday villas. It is not only easy to pass off a rolled up cabbage leaf as a spear of asparagus but baby will respect you so much more as a parent if you display ingenuity and economic sense.

A Menu Planner

So with these three fundamental principles in mind, let's look at how to plan your baby's weaning menu.

Breakfast

Always start with a turnip. This is a powerful metaphor for doing what needs to be done right up front in the day. 'Labour ye first, and then enjoy the fruits of your labours' as I think the Bible ought to have said. You really must be strict about ensuring your baby finishes the turnip before he's allowed to eat anything else. You can puree the turnip or serve it thinly sliced, but DO NOT roast it. Roasting makes it more pleasant to eat and therefore destroys the point of the metaphor.

While baby is eating turnip you can embrace the wonderful opportunity to act by example and roll up your sleeves to accomplish a challenging but rewarding task – thus demonstrating the turnip metaphor in practice. Perhaps you can do the ironing, clean the silver, or sort out the household bills.

After turnip, think about the historical dietary precedent that will inspire your child. Look to the emerging superpowers of Brazil, China or India. A dish of rice and beans, curry or stir fry will convey the verve and brio of a fresh dawn, a bright future – and crucially give your child a sense of *belonging* to that vision.

LUNCH

This is a meal where you can help to build resolve in your child after any setbacks the morning might have brought. My inspiration here is the British Empire – if boiled ham and jam roly-poly secured India then surely this diet will grow a bright new generation who will persevere to find the cure for Alzheimer's.

AFTERNOON TEA

What a wonderful opportunity to introduce culture and beauty via French patisserie. You will also be cleverly showing baby that although France is wonderful for a bit of creative indulgence, it is hardly the foundation for robust socio-economic progress and therefore won't be found in my breakfast, lunch or supper recipes. Afternoon tea is wonderful for developing hand-eye co-ordination – clasping those miniature macaroons will accelerate baby towards holding a pen and writing poetry. This meal is also a wonderful avenue for managing discipline – babies quickly understand that unnecessary crying earlier in the day means no pistachio mille feuille in the afternoon.

SUPPER

German recipes are very useful here. After a long day, meals which promote a strong manufacturing sector and stable stock market will provide baby with the strength and security to sleep through the night. Pureed sauerkraut and Gulaschsuppe fill the stomach and the heart with resolve.

Needless to say I have a range of cookbooks available at www.helpfulhumour.com and I'm sure Waitrose are on the cusp of accepting my delicious range of ready meals. For the truly committed amongst you I also run the Angelica Fustain™ Chef franchise. Simply dial the number and in no time at all a fully trained chef will be at your door, ready to rustle up a wonderful meal for baby. (Please note I am legally obliged to tell you that the number is premium rate, and by 'in no time at all' I mean within three working days – excluding weekends and bank holidays).

THE EATING ENVIRONMENT

Mealtime settings are almost as important as the food itself. A properly laid table with floral centrepiece, tablecloth and place mats nurtures the soul. Cleanliness is next to godliness, so crisp ironed linen napkins and sparkling crystal are essential.

But what do we find in a typical new parent's kitchen? A mountain of ghastly plastic! No wonder little Timmykins is throwing food; if *you* were given a Disney Princess melamine bowl and a bendy spoon, you would throw them at someone's head, wouldn't you? Parents pretend that their use of plastic is motivated by 'health and safety' when this is quite blatantly a thin excuse for protecting their good china. Show your baby right from the start that you expect him to grow up and dine in Michelin Star restaurants and it will become a self-fulfilling prophecy. An 18 year old who has been used to finger bowls and soup spoons from an early age exudes that kind of self-assured gravitas that top league Universities look for at interview. Yes of course there will be the odd breakage, but as you see your favourite fin-de-siècle Wedgewood milk jug crash to the ground and shatter in a thousand pieces think of it as a vital investment just like a proper car seat, private education, or a quality barber.

A word on cutlery: it can be embarrassing for a baby when their fine motor skills are insufficiently developed to wield a knife and fork properly. So many parents fall into the trap of letting baby use a spoon, or even worse, their hands. I know it's tempting, but it's a tragic blunder. You might as well give them a sleeping bag for their future park bench now. The sensible solution to juvenile mal-coordination is a set of Angelica Fustain™ cutlery gloves. The solid silver cutlery is lovingly hand sewn into the gloves. Simply pop the gloves onto baby and hey presto! Despite his flailing arms, baby is in command of a knife and fork. I am currently battling with the Health and Safety department at Harrods, but hope to introduce the baby fork glove and baby knife glove very soon. Yes of course there is a tiny, tiny danger that the knife point might make a little bit of a stab in junior's face but I firmly believe that they will learn quickly. Wrapping babies up in cotton wool will only undermine their self-esteem and independence.

CONCLUSION

I trust that this chapter has shown you the huge importance of weaning correctly. In case you are in any doubt as to the vital necessity of my approach, I will leave you with this salutary tale:

I saw two teenagers eating whilst waiting for the bus the other day. One was munching on a burger, ketchup oozing down his fingers, mouth open as he chatted to a group of 'mates'. The other was quietly reading a book on astrophysics, and carrying a violin case, with a neat Tupperware on his lap containing a sensible array of items for a packed lunch. Note – he was not *eating* his lunch, obviously he knew that a bus stop bench was an inappropriate place to repast. What struck me was how clearly the correlation between proper food and mental development was laid out for all to see. What other conclusion can one draw, but that structured eating from an early age produces young adults with intelligence and diligence, whereas fast food creates a slovenly personality? Good luck with your turnip-led weaning, and if ever you falter in your resolve, may that image of the two teenagers spur you on to starch your napkins properly.

CHAPTER SIX

CLOTHING

Clothes provide more than just warmth and protection, they are key indicators of intelligence and social class. I passionately believe that the clothes we choose for our children have a direct and significant impact on their future success in life. In this chapter I'll give you clear advice on what baby should be wearing at each age and explain the importance of colour and texture throughout this sartorial journey. I'll then look at clothes management and maintenance.

THE EARLY MONTHS – SWADDLING VERSUS FAILURE

There is huge debate about the merits of swaddling. Some say it is an outdated approach akin to Chinese foot-binding. I say it provides just the kind of structure and discipline which we so desperately need for today's youth. The tragedy is that most people are simply getting swaddling wrong, and this is giving inaccurate support to the naysayers' lies. There are merely 25 easy steps to the perfect swaddle. I've included them all in my exclusive Angelica Fustain™ swaddle kit, which is a bargain at only £5.69, but I here I'm going to share with you 5 key steps of the key 25 steps that really are key:

1. Use pure llama wool for your swaddling material. You can send your husband to South America (I offer a discount package including flights, accommodation and a four day course on baby swaddling yoga massage for £1200 per person. Sadly we are unable to accommodate children on this package). This can be a wonderful way of saying thank you to your husband for fathering your child and it can be the perfect break for them in the last weeks of pregnancy when you are getting tetchy and difficult. You can also purchase additional llama wool material direct from my website at £49.99 per yard, or £29.99 for the raw wool and a discounted spindle and spinning wheel for only £299.99.

2. Hand wash the material at least four times before using and in the penultimate wash add a quarter of a tea spoon of gentleman's relish. The calming aroma of the anchovy paste is a little-known weapon against colic, and reduces the chances of child-snatching in

shopping malls, but do remember to sell your cats before using this approach as they have been known to confuse an anchovy-swaddled baby with a luxury Felix snack pouch. I am unable to comment on individual cases, but suffice it to say that I am putting it to Lord Justice McEwan in the current case in the High Court that I have made this *quite clear* in all my marketing literature

3. Cut the material into 3.3 mm strips and then sew back together into 3.3 cm strips – remember, the greater the effort the more your child will love you. The value here is the flexibility and strength of the resulting swaddling bands.

4. Swaddle baby from magnetic south to north. Remember to keep a compass in your changing bag at all times.

5. When pushing a swaddled child in the pram, remember always to move in an easterly or westerly direction. When needing to travel north or south, simply tack as a windsurfer would in a zigzag pattern from east to west. This has the double benefit of being a wonderful toner for thighs and rears.

Swaddled babies are healthier, happier and less likely to have cellulite. They are more likely to go on to be Chief Executives, Graduates and Doctors, and to sponsor the theatre and the fine arts. Although my publishers insist I point out that in a strictly legal capacity I am unable to verify any of these claims, I am utterly confident on these points.

After swaddling: what next?

It's best to make a clean break from swaddling to normal clothes. I believe the current trend for skinny jeans is because this advice simply wasn't given to our parents and we have a generation confused about the appropriate tightness of clothing. But don't eat yourself up inside by blaming your parents; remember I wasn't here to help in their day. Take a positive step instead: sit down and write an anger journal listing all the things they did wrong. It makes such a wonderfully honest birthday or Christmas present. I've found it's that bit more impactful if you detail the journal with photographs of difficult times in your life and painful anecdotes so you can give tangible examples of the pain they've caused and have robust conversations to address their failures.

…but I digress!

By 3 months baby should be wearing underpants, trousers and a shirt. Baby needs to understand the importance of being well turned out as it has such a big impact on civil order. A development which truly concerns me is the worrying trend for T shirts with slogans for young babies. I saw 'future DJ' the other day and 'future rock star'. Think carefully about the kinds of subliminal messages you want to be sending your child. Is it really appropriate for them to be wearing a top without a collar?

The psychological impact of different colours is significant; indeed I believe it is woven into our DNA.

For example, the vermillion appearance of a footballer's wife is a highly effective warning signal in exactly the same way that red berries signify poison in the wild. The lower classes and divorcees' affection for leopard skin and leather trousers comes from an atavistic yearning for the stability of a clan structure in our hunter-gatherer days. I've had a surprising lack of support for my theory from the Association of Nannies and Childminders, but it seems self-evident that every child needs to understand their history and development if they are going to excel in the modern world. It is from this strong academic framework that I've developed the following month-by-month colour and texture developmental wardrobe guide:

3 – 6 MONTHS

Early days baby wear is inspired by the terracotta of caves: think muted night time Babygros, clay-coloured trousers, earthen-hued shirts. Toward the end of this period you can start introducing greys as an unconscious reminder of the invention of flint tools. Increase the power of the subliminal messaging by making baby's life a little bit easier and more comfortable at the same time – perhaps serve food a little quicker or introduce more interesting toys to underline the wonderful impact of tools on early human living standards.

6 – 9 MONTHS

Now is the time for the burnt sienna tones of the savannah. Make sure baby has elasticated waists as the primeval parts of his brain remember the freedom of movement while mankind migrated from Africa across the globe. Start to introduce bronze fastenings, animal pelts and rudimentary weaving. Keep pictures or designs very simple – think cave paintings of gazelle and mammoth.

9-14 MONTHS
By now baby understands the themes and you can speed up the process – be bold! Be creative! Medieval-inspired embroidery, chain mail, whalebone corsetry and layered undergarments are all great for this age. Remember to focus on the higher socio-economic fabrics – think silk and velvet rather than sack cloth. By experimenting with the types of clothing as well as the colour and texture you are helping your baby to understand mankind's moral development through the metaphor of tailoring. It saddens me to see so many of today's babies in a uniform of baby Gap tracksuits – as if the world were one vast baseball-player-manufacturing-unit. Where are the ruffs? The wimples? The doublet and hose? The wasted opportunity for this age group to learn and grow is horrifying.

14 TO 19 MONTHS
This stage is crucial. Now is the time to segue carefully from a period of blacks and greys to signify the industrial revolution into an explosion of technological revolution colour. Yes it is frustrating that many clothing ranges are 12-18 months, rather than 14-19, but this is yet another wonderful opportunity for you to show your devotion

to your child by going against the herd of ill-conceived parenting habits so common amongst your peers. And help is at hand. You can buy my 'Clothes through the Ages' book (the title is a wonderful play on words that I am rather proud of!) It gives countless patterns you can use to make your own hand-made clothes. My particular favourites are the Lady Jane Grey head dress for 10 month olds and the Isambard Kingdom Brunel waistcoat, trousers and top hat ensemble for 15 month olds. Really very simple to make and the results are quite enchanting! Alternatively you can buy a range of Angelica Fustain™ ready-made clothes from www.helpfulhumour.com, all reassuringly priced at between £25 and £85 to make sure you never see a child emerge from Aldi wearing the same outfit your offspring is wearing. All items are hand-wash only.

Finally, a note on shoes: As your child starts to walk make sure you invest in the sturdiest, most robust shoes you can. My mother never skimped on 1970s Start Right models and my years of dealing with classmates calling me 'turd feet' have given me the emotional backbone one needs in this world – to say what needs to be said and not overly rely on fickle 'friendship'. I do not see my peers – who frequented C&A and River Island for their footwear – enjoying the same success. Their collapsed arches are a fitting metaphor for their moral standing in society now.

Clothes maintenance and management

At a stage when your child is growing so fast it is imperative that your clothes management system is second to none. Colicky babies who are reputedly struggling with teething are often just unsettled by the disorder in their chest of drawers or the unsightly stain on the heel of their sock. As a parent it's tempting to think 'I've got the important things right, the odd un-ironed Babygro really isn't going to matter,' but put yourself in your newborn's shoes... they are doubtless panicking, 'if mummy and daddy can't even get the very simple things right then how on earth are they going to choose an appropriate school for me or achieve that delicate balance of a loving yet firm parenting style of discipline that I crave so much?'

Don't worry, simply follow my straightforward advice and all will be well:

Clothes washing, drying and ironing

Busy mums make terrible blunders such as putting the bins out on the wrong day or forgetting to pay their local resident association fees. Spending a few hours each day washing and ironing is a wonderful way of keeping calm and meditative so you can remember the important things in life. For example: inhale as you put the washing into the machine, exhale as you load the soap dispenser; breathe in as you place the iron onto the garment and breathe out as you glide it away from you. Visualise your stress ebbing away as you push the steam button. Why not say some powerful affirmations to yourself too?

- 'I am a useful member of society'
- 'The more effort I put in, the more my child loves me'
- 'Day by day, in every way, Angelica Fustain is helping me to become a perfectly adequate parent'

I thoroughly recommend you invest in at least two washing machines – so you have one machine for grown up clothes and one for your baby. If you don't your poor husband will have to expend needless mental anguish on the possibility that his Ralph Lauren chinos might have brushed against a part of the washing machine that has had previous contact with baby trousers which have been next to a nappy. Poor man! Of course the ideal is to have one washing machine for each member of the family, but I do realise that some of you might have utility rooms which are on the small side.

You also obviously need a large Belfast sink for all the hand washing. I know that modern washing machines have a 'hand wash' setting, but I refuse to believe that baby doesn't know the difference between an item washed by a machine and an item washed with the loving hands of a mother. In a similar vein: by all means use a tumble dryer for towels and sheets, but you can enhance the parent-child bond quite magically by singing your children's clothes dry with your warm breath. 'It's like being dressed in mummy's kisses' I imagine a child might think. If you feel your singing isn't of a good enough quality, then an alternative method is to buy Swiss mountain air – you can buy canisters on my website for just £74 each. You can really tell the difference between an outfit which has been dried in urban smog and the crisp freshness of one hand blow-dried with alpine purity.

CLOTHES FOLDING AND STORAGE

I like to continue the North to South swaddling theme and fold all my clothes in a Northerly direction, but as long as you are consistent in your compass bearings, I think Easterly is fine as well. In terms of cupboard management just remember to get the basics right: lining paper for the drawers, lavender bags for girls and rosewood for boys. Thereafter the key thing is labelling. Make sure each drawer is clearly marked with the overall heading (e.g. 'socks') and then a detailed inventory of all the items and their status (i.e. 'present' 'being worn' 'in the wash' and so forth). This will make it so much easier when baby takes responsibility for dressing themselves at around 18 months. Do also make full use of the wonderful organisational gadgets at Lakeland Plastic. In the kitchen I simply don't know how I lived without their 'bagel coral' for holding bagels to slice, their vegetable cushions and their mushroom brushes, and in the realm of clothing storage they are simply visionary. I hesitate to recommend their sock tidies and tight interweavers as doubtless by the time this book goes to press all manner of wonderful new

Lakeland inventions will have redefined standards yet again. Who knows, I am still dreaming of the day when they are able to stock one of my weekly suggestions to them (including an electric rotating shoe dispenser), but I bow to their superior knowledge when they state that they simply don't feel they can do my ideas justice in the manufacturing process. Such professionals!

Clothes maintenance

There is a very narrow window when clothes actually fit. It saddens me to see children with turn ups so large it hinders their movement, or tight tops with a little too much décolletage as is seemly for a seven month old. Make a quick daily inventory of items that are too small and burn them immediately. I am all for recycling, but children can be deeply traumatised by seeing their cast offs worn by another child. As for clothes which are a little too large – make it a part of your evening wind down to readjust hems on a daily basis. When a child fits their clothes perfectly they feel they fit the world perfectly, they feel comfortable in their niche, and what greater gift can a parent give to their child and to society at large?

Conclusion

I hope I've adequately explained why clothes are such a vital ingredient in a baby's emotional and spiritual development and your duties as parents in managing their early wardrobe. I will leave you with this salutary tale about an area we haven't spoken much about, namely the dangers of fancy dress – a supposedly 'fun' and 'light hearted' avenue of clothing that can actually lead to deep emotional scars:

Our local church runs a delightful Christmas Carol service and children are allowed to come in appropriate fancy dress to join in the re-enactment of the Nativity story. Imagine the universal horror last year when amongst the 'animals in the stable' was noticed a child in a blue and green spotted 'Monster Inc: the movie' outfit. Not only is that child growing up with a very warped understanding of the Christian story (and the wider local population of children now believe that Jesus killed off all the dinosaurs) but isn't it mind blowing that more mothers don't grab the quite obvious opportunity to encourage entrepreneurship in the next generation by dressing their children up as the inn keeper? Such a shame...

Chapter Seven

Stimulation

The latest genetic research indicates that there is still a lot you can do to develop your child, even if your gene pool is a little lacking in finesse. But there has been a worrying trend towards 'Tiger Mothers' so in this chapter I hope to give a gentle steer on what is appropriate and what is unpalatably pushy. The vital difference is not *what* you do, but *how* you do it. Let's take the notional example of two mothers:

MOTHER A wakes her child at 5 a.m. to drive to a special pre-school Sudoku and Swimming class that is only available in a community centre 50 miles away. She is tired and grumpy and a bit worried that she's over-cooking things. She snaps at her toddler for crying, the child feels under pressure and grows up to become a drug addict.

MOTHER B rouses her child cheerfully with a freshly baked muffin. The clock says 7 a.m. and Mother B smiles to herself because her 18 month old doesn't know mummy changed the time on the clock to maintain a sense of calm routine, and that it is actually 5 a.m. As they sing their favourite nursery rhymes in the car and play 'I spy with my little eye, a native English deciduous shrub beginning with 'o'' Mother B thanks her child for the special time together and then they joyfully skip into the Sudoku and Swimming class hand in hand. The child grows up to become the next Carol Vorderman – but one with a more appropriate cleavage and skirt length.

You see? Just a little thought can make a huge difference. In this chapter I've divided the types of infant stimulation into 3 categories:

1. Structured group activities. It is so important for children to socialise from an early age. They need to start to compare themselves with others and understand their place in the future pecking order.
2. Active conversation with your child – robust conversation which will help them not only to learn to speak, but crucially learn to speak *sensible content*
3. One to one activities for you and your child. You need focused time spent away from cooking, cleaning and supporting your husband
4. Independent play. Your child needs to be a self-starter if they have any hope of buying their own house before the age of 35.

1. Structured group activities

If you want to get your child into the best schools, start thinking IMMEDIATLY about developing their CVs. Music and Yoga for the under ones are non-negotiable essentials these days, so is swimming, and rightly so, but I do want to sound a note of caution. It is currently the vogue to photograph your baby swimming underwater. Yes it is wonderful that they are so confident, but it is a little startling to walk into someone's kitchen and be confronted with a 12 x 6 foot canvass on the wall showing a semi naked child staring at out in a – frankly – unhinged fashion. I worry that it also encourages an unhealthy desire to pursue synchronised swimming in later life.

But I digress...

To stand out from the crowd you really must include a couple more activities into their pre-school years. Here are some suggestions:

MANDARIN. 'Coo' and 'Ah Goo' are essential phonic building blocks for Chinese fluency. It can be so frustrating for children when their first tentative steps towards international power are met with pathetic oohs and ahs from their parents. Learn the language yourself in your spare time.

ELECTRONICS. All too often I see babies with a natural affinity for Advanced Electronics being thwarted by appalling parenting. Does your baby crawl towards sockets? Like chewing on wiring? Common wisdom would have you believe that they are merely creating danger for themselves, but look more closely and many of them are desperately trying to point out to you that you have an inappropriate fuse for the appliance.

OLYMPIC PREPARATION. Take an educated guess about which country will be hosting the Olympics when your child is 18 (my hunch for the 2028 hosts is Uzbekistan–mining revenues and a strong government are a powerful combination). Now organise coaching for your preschooler in the country's national sport. You will thereby be ensuring that Junior is the obvious choice to represent Great Britain when the sport becomes an Olympic discipline in the future. Your peers may raise eyebrows that you have set up intensive jousting/mud wrestling/elk hunting classes for your child, but you will have the last laugh 18 years from now when he wins Gold and in his post-podium interview tearfully thanks his mother for her vision and courage.

Now we have looked at structured activities, let us move on to the second category:

2. INVIGORATING ONE TO ONE CONVERSATION

All too often one sees babies being patronised with nonsense chit-chat of the 'who's a good baby diddums shall we go in the prammy wammy?' variety. Ghastly! Grasp the opportunity to engage with your children more proactively. Here are some of my favourite discussion topics which will both entertain and stimulate your child:

WHAT WOULD JANE AUSTEN SAY?

As the day unfolds simply ask the question, 'What would Jane Austen say?' The joy of this game is that it can turn even the most ordinary event into an entertainment. For example, a car draws up outside your house. Ask out loud to your baby:

> "What would Jane Austen say…? Perhaps: *What manner of transportation is this? Is it a barouche to transport us to the delights of a ball where we can choreograph our feelings in tune to the step of a polka?'*"

Obviously you have an advantage over your baby: both in terms of your knowledge of Pride and Prejudice and in terms of you being able to speak. But herein lies the beauty of the game. Before you know it, the years will have flown by and your little one, now a toddler, well trained by years of practice, will reply:

> *'Why no, Mama, it is but our unseemly neighbours in a mode of transport most unbecoming to their station, come to enquire about the possibility of a play date. Make haste and let us repair to the Morning Room where we can take up some urgent needlework and avert the impending social catastrophe.'*

Children learn through play and this game cleverly helps them to explore social hierarchy, manners, history and literature whilst also expanding their vocabulary and conversational skills. Perfect!

HOW MANY POTATOES WOULD IT TAKE?

This is a wonderful way of developing baby's spatial awareness. Point to, say, the table and ask,

'How many potatoes would it take to build that table?'

The joy of this conversational gambit is that it can take you in so many directions:

- You can ponder on the *size* of potato you might use – a small New Potato or a large baking one for example – and teach baby about 'small', 'bigger' and 'big'. Is the table suitable for an informal supper or could it cater for a full dinner party, and what are the consequences of that for us as a successful family unit?
- You can explore the variety of *shapes* – the difference between rhomboids, spheres and trapezohedra. I had the pleasure of visiting a particularly precocious baby whose first word was 'dodecahedron'. Sadly the parents mistook this for 'daddy' but thank goodness they invested in a Angelica Fustain™ certified nanny for the next 10 years and little Timmy is now president of the school chess club. I am so proud.

- The suitability of different building *materials*. The suitability of fluffy Maris Piper versus smooth Desiree – or indeed mahogany or pine!! These early discussions help baby to understand that thy have huge potential control over their external environment and encourage them to think about how they will design the interior of their substantial Grade II listed home in years to come.

- The fleeting nature of *beauty and substance* – the wax and wane of organic matter. For bright babies I thoroughly recommend introducing them to Brian Cox at this stage so they can start to comprehend the mysteries of the universe. My editors have warned me that it is perhaps a teensiest weeniest bit premature to offer you a personal introduction to Brian, as we haven't actually met yet. However, I feel absolutely sure that he'll be as excited as I am by my plans for joint sponsorship of a pre-school Star Gazers Club. I have a vision of little ones in a Church Hall singing 'twinkle twinkle little star' and then the Group Leader (a CRB checked Brian Cox lookalike who has paid a very reasonable fee to the Angelica Fustain™ Franchise to get a comprehensive starter pack including session plans on laminated cards) asking the children 'what makes the star twinkle?' The Leader then segues effortlessly into a charming introduction to organic chemistry for the under threes.

...But I digress...

These are but a few of the discussion avenues you can pursue with the 'how many potatoes?' game. We haven't even touched on basic engineering principles involved in making a table, how to display firm but fair leadership when managing a team of furniture builders…the list goes on and on.

3. One to One activities for you and your child

I know that in the early days your child won't yet have the hand to eye co-ordination for table tennis or needlework. Be patient, these special bonding opportunities are just round the corner. In the meantime there is still so much you can do, such as:

- Chess – simply strap them into a chair and move the pieces for them, discussing tactics and options as you go along.
- Wood carving. Of course knives are sharp and one should take care, but as long as you're not silly and attempt something ambitious like mahogany, it really shouldn't be a problem. Working with pine can be both instructive and therapeutic.
- Sudoku – in the few months before your child is able to read numbers you can easily create a vegetable Sudoku grid. Simply pop a certain number of carrot sticks or broccoli florets into each square, put a bowl of spare vegetables at the side and help junior to fit the appropriate number of vegetables into the missing

spaces. Of course once you've filled the grid correctly you can allow your little one to eat the vegetables as a 'well done' treat

4. INDEPENDENT PLAY

Independent play is crucial to ensure your child is a self-starter, but I want to introduce a note of caution before we dive in. Even young babies realise that toys are usually a poor substitute for a parent's attention and an overuse of toys can massively damage their self-esteem. Ask yourself if you are *consciously* giving them time for independent play or merely fobbing them off. Of course you will sometimes need to use them to entertain baby when you are cooking a nutritious meal or doing essential tasks like starching the napkins, but for the rest of the time *do* engage your baby in the stimulating discussions and activities outlined in the previous sections. If you find yourself sitting down and having a cup of tea that is a good indication that you are veering towards the 'fobbing off' end of the spectrum.

One challenge with independent play is how to assess whether your child is getting it right or not. For example, when making mud pies, are they continually finessing the approach they will use as the next Jamie Oliver, or are they simply messing around? Unfortunately when you try to observe your child they typically want you to join in, which undermines the whole point about independent play.

Don't worry, simply follow my foolproof steps:

Firstly, explain your expectations and boundaries very clearly to your baby as follows:

> 'I am leaving you to play by yourself for 10 minutes. Enjoy this opportunity to learn and explore independently. I will be hanging out the washing and although we normally do this together and reflect on the different materials such as cotton and wool and their properties I am going to do this by myself now so that I can have some special mummy time to recharge my batteries'.

Firmly close the door behind you, head to the utility room and then *monitor them on a CCTV you have installed throughout the house!* Track what they are doing and log your finds on a laptop. My Angelica Fustain™ house-monitoring kit is a snip at £1275 (plus installation charges). I also have available the Angelica Fustain™ baby-tracker database, which comes with a range of pre-loaded reports and data point summaries. You can print out findings as bar charts or Venn diagrams to be shared with friends and family and once laminated they make fabulous Birthday and Christmas presents. The database is a bargain at only £275.99 for three licenses.

Now you understand the steps to setting up solitary activity, let's look at what toys are best to promote healthy independent play.

I do have a specific bee in my bonnet about teddy bears and soft toys. There's a strange tendency for them to be half dressed – bunny rabbits with jumpers and nothing else, ducks sporting just a hat or elephants in tutus with nothing covering the pre-breast area. If your child shares his cot with a teddy bear sporting just a bow tie you might as well drive him straight to the local strip club. But more importantly – in addition to the particular point about soft toys – I want to raise the alarm more generally about toys. Toy manufacturers have created a vicious spiral: advertising things you do not need and then creating products with built-in obsolescence so you need to keep on buying.

All a baby really needs is: cardboard boxes, mud, water, whatever everyday items are immediately at hand. Let's look at each of these in turn.

Cardboard Boxes
Sadly today's cardboard boxes have vicious staples and serrated edges which renders them unsuitable. Luckily I have brought out a range of Angelica Fustain™ safe boxes, free from sharp edges and held together with organic, edible glue. For just £5.99 a box they give you peace of mind that your little one is having safe, innocent play, untainted by unscrupulous toy manufacturers. Please note that the boxes come in plastic wrappers which do present a choking hazard and must be discarded safely. Please also not that the term 'safe box' does not imply that it is safe to store anything *in* the boxes. They are for

playing with only and certainly not for transporting items. But I digress…

MUD

Mud can be hard to come by in today's world. Obviously it is highly inappropriate to source if from your garden because it might damage the plants and it is so important that all neighbours work together to create mutually beneficial vistas. The local park is one option, but do watch out for dog poo. My Angelica Fustain™ soil testing kit is only £48.98 and allows you to make sure the park mud is healthy and safe. In just 12 simple steps taking under an hour you can analyse the soil using approaches that are easy to follow for anyone with a standard A grade in GCSE Chemistry. The other alternative is my Angelica Fustain™ mud substitute. Each 1kg bag costs £12.99, plus postage and packing. Simply build a sandpit-style container, add water and voila, innocent care-free fun is at your child's fingertips every day.

WATER

Don't fall victim to French bottled water. Tap water is absolutely fine for child's play. Do think carefully about *where* you let your child play with water. By all means use a bath, but I would counsel against plastic baths – entombing your baby in cheap modern synthetic material can't be healthy. Roll top cast iron baths are the way forward. It's also imperative to have two baths – one for washing and one for play. When young children confuse hygiene with entertainment all hell breaks use. No wonder teenagers today go to discothèque 'bubble parties'.

I expect your house has carefully coordinated ornaments and soft furnishings and you may be horrified at the thought of your baby playing with items which you have spent hours organising into what looks like effortless chic. I therefore suggest you buy pretend 'everyday items' for your child to play with. Wooden spoons, pine cones, balls of wool, tin buckets are all ideal. I have gone to the trouble of packaging them up into my Angelica Fustain™ 'everyday non-toy stimulation items' kit at just £35.65.

CONCLUSION

So in conclusion, don't just idly relax and enjoy playtime with your child – if you feel a slight frisson of nervousness that you should be doing more and are somehow inadequate you are probably on the right track. Cast your minds back to Mother A and Mother B from the start of this chapter. If you are like Mother A, putting her child to bed grumpy and tired each night, then get inspired by Mother B. her child simply thinks it's part of a normal bedtime routine to practice synchronized swimming in the bath and make her own bed (ie literally, with hammer and nails from scratch) before cheerfully bidding mama goodnight in Latin. Just a little bit of effort reaps such dividends.

Chapter Eight

Discipline

Discipline is so important, but let me be clear right from the start that I have no time for discipline *just for the sake of it*. My father was caned regularly and arbitrarily at school, including once merely for sneezing whilst walking up the stairs. All this achieved was to give him a heart breaking phobia of both pepper and stairwells which meant I unjustly endured a childhood of bland food in a bungalow.

I also detest pseudo-discipline for show – by that I mean the performance parenting one hears in the supermarket along the lines of:

'Timmy I have asked you not to kick me because it hurts mummy, but you have done it again so there will be no homemade frozen yogurt tonight now and you need to give your pocket money to the Orphanage in Vietnam.'

It only takes once glance into the mother's trolley at the mountain of crisps and chocolate to confirm:

- She is pathetically showing off in front of other shoppers. Timmy will absolutely be getting a king size pack of Doritos for tea.
- She will try and disguise her weakness by explaining that these are *not* crisps as they are corn-based rather than potato-based.
- Timmy is not a fool. Timmy will quickly learn that his mother is a terrible disciplinarian. This will evolve into a general contempt for authority. Timmy will be into crack cocaine by 12, rioting by 14 and money laundering by 16.

The stakes are perilously high readers; one simple slip up from you and the moral fabric of the whole nation is at risk. So in this chapter I am going to show you two simple things:

1. What constitutes 'good behaviour'.
2. How to discipline children so that they perform these good behaviours.

1. GOOD BEHAVIOUR

It is extremely simple. There are five clear behaviours we need from children:

- cleanliness
- manners
- respect for elders and betters

- tidiness
- peace and quiet

I was tempted to stray into religion in this chapter, but my publisher banned me on the grounds that it is (and I quote:) 'Both a minefield, and very uncool'. What a shame, I think religion has been given a spectacularly bad press. I'm not sure I actually believe in God, – I can't quite see how an all-powerful Lord would see the need for melamine, nylon, or Jeremy Clarkson in his creation – but religions have given the world some wonderful things – such as beautiful architecture, paintings and poetry. Surely even the most confirmed of atheists can't help but be moved by Sarah Brightman signing Piu Jesu? Although what on earth she saw in Andrew Lloyd Webber, goodness only knows.

But I digress…

Let me give you a little more detail on each of the five essential behavioural goals:

CLEANLINESS

Few people were taught adequate physical hygiene as a child. You only have to inhale the body odour on any form of public transport to understand the terrible consequences of this. I am completely reliant on anti-histamines during the summer months – not because of hay fever, but to combat the ill effects of 'Eau de Beckham' clashing with 'Essence of Beyoncé' or whatever they are on the local bus. Instilling good cleanliness behaviours from babyhood onwards is every parent's duty.

As a starting point, simply ensure hand washing after going to the lavatory, using public transport, touching any animal, touching another human (especially grandparents), touching any surface or material (especially trousers), before and after touching face or mouth, before and after eating and before and after sleeping.

In terms of what to clean *with* simply use old-fashioned soap. Avoid the pointless modern hand-pump liquid soaps; they are simply a license for manufacturers to print money. This will mean you need to take bars of soap with you wherever you go, but don't worry; I've designed a carrying-case on a chain which doubles up as a rather charming pendant for only £19.99. it is available, as ever, at www.helpfulhumour.com.

MANNERS AND ETIQUETTE

Today manners and etiquette are sadly dismissed as superficial or old fashioned. I asked a recent client if her three year old would know how to address a Baronet as opposed to a Lord and she honestly thought I was joking. But manners are the bedrock of civilisation; they oil the wheels as we struggle to live together on an overcrowded planet. Just yesterday I was chatting to a mother whose child wanted a pony party – a horrendously stressful experience for her. The Trekking centre only allows 12 people, but could the mother get people to RSVP in a timely fashion? – No!

Poor manners have actively contributed to that poor woman's reliance on Valium. Yes of course one could argue that her reliance on Valium contributed to the poor management of party replies, but I think that is grossly unfair. Key behaviours to instil in pre-schoolers include: the appropriate use of 'please', 'thank you', 'how enchanting to meet you', basic bowing and curtseying and the correct pronunciation of 'ma'am'.

RESPECT FOR ELDERS AND BETTERS

Just because everyone is the same in the eyes of the law and of God doesn't mean everyone's current behaviour is acceptable. I sincerely hope that the tramp who frequents our local park will go to heaven if there is one – despite his tiresome propensity for camping on the bench with the best view – as his behaviour doubtless stemmed from terrible parenting. I do, however, passionately believe that Jesus would give him a thorough wash and stop him shouting obscenities before letting him through any Pearly Gates.

Right from the start you need to guide your child to admire the right role models and avoid life's lame ducks. Clothes are a terrifically important clue: structured tailoring, linen and wool usually indicate good character; free-flowing garments in nylon suggest mental weakness. I have developed a handy 'friend or foe' app to help you. Download the app for just £6.99, take a discreet photo of the potential friend/teacher/scout leader and the app will instantly give you a snap decision. My legal advisers have forced me to note that this could be construed as defamation of character, which although not a criminal offence could entangle you in an unpleasant civil suit, so I need to position this app as a 'harmless piece of fun'.

TIDINESS

Tidiness encourages a plethora of wonderful life skills such as good planning, attention to detail, persistence and vision. My grandmother used to say: 'Tidy hairstyle, tidy mind' and I so agree. It can't be a coincidence that Margaret Thatcher's hair was always a fortress of lacquer. I do not think she could have secured Britain's EU rebate if she had waltzed in to negotiations with a flyaway fringe. It is a fallacy that children are untidy. That is a product of slovenly parenting. Give them clear goals and the rest should follow. Simply ask your pre-schooler to help you sort the toys into their alphabetically-ordered storage system every night. Not only is this instilling a core personality trait, it is also a wonderful opportunity to learn the alphabet and stimulate fascinating conversation. "Should this toy Thomas the Tank Engine go into 'T' for 'train' or 'L' for 'locomotive' or indeed 'M' for 'mode of transport'?" The evenings will fly by.

PEACE AND QUIET

One cannot go to a café, museum or even National Trust property these days without encountering a sign proudly proclaiming that it is a 'child-friendly' venue. I can bear the brightly coloured plastic in these establishments, I can bear the dumbed-down menu, I can even bear the baby-changing mat in the ladies lavatory – which is invariably badly placed so one has to do an awkward tango from soap dispenser to hand drier in order to avoid faecal matter – but I *cannot* stand the noise.

I have written to the British Medical Association with a carefully reasoned essay pointing out that a key, overlooked reason for the increase in heart disease today must be toddler noise. It leads to pent up anger and anxiety that eats away at the arteries and overloads our beloved NHS. For those less fortunate than myself who don't have easy access to a weekly yoga-lates class the consequences can be devastating. Teach your child the value of silence and stillness and I strongly believe you will not only be raising a wonderful young person, you will be saving the precious institution that is the National Health Service.

2. HOW TO DISCIPLINE

Now we've looked at the five key behavioural goals, we can start to look at *how* to discipline. I thoroughly recommend doing a degree in Law so you can properly weigh up the different merits of a justice system based on retribution versus reformation. I am expecting to hear back from Oxford University any day now regarding my proposals for them to run – for an extremely reasonable fee – an Angelica Fustain™ BA hons course in toddler justice.

There are four steps to my simple system of toddler justice:

STEP ONE
Be very clear about what you are asking your child to do

or not do. Notice the difference in the statements below for example:

- 'Come here' vs 'Crawl to the x I have marked on the floor with tape, stop there and await further instructions'
- 'Be quiet' vs 'Keep to a volume equal to or less than nine decibels for the next seven minutes.'

STEP TWO
Explain the consequences and your intentions. Don't be afraid to do this right from the start, it's never too early to communicate clearly: For example:

- 'If you haven't mastered the art of rolling over by six months, I will tilt your bed by 45 degrees at alternate hours during the night. This is purely to prevent your peers rejecting you as a runt, and ensure I don't go off you.'
- 'If you refuse boiled turnip this meal, I will give you raw turnip for your next meal. This is to toughen you up to endure the inevitable hardship life will bring and to breed the determination required to succeed.'

STEP THREE
Stick to your boundaries; follow through on consequences you've laid out. Sadly for most children these days the word 'no' is rescinded so often they become immune to it. Even if you remain resolute there are countless friends,

relatives and preschool activity leaders who won't. You must therefore create your own special vocabulary. I use the word 'armadillo' in place of 'no' and for children under my wing 'armadillo' clearly means absolutely, irrefutably a line not to be crossed. Yes it was unfortunate when I took a two year old to the zoo last year and they had a bit of a breakdown by the armadillo enclosure, but they are responding very well to treatment and I believe this one hiccup is evidence of a tiny risk worth taking in an otherwise faultless approach.

Step four

Now praise or punish as appropriate:

* ### Praise

  Why do dolphins jump in Aquariums? They jump for a fish, but jump even higher on the *possibility* that they might just get a huge fish…even though *they don't always*. Irregular, marginally erratic praise is vital with both dolphins and children. I don't mean vengeful, mercurial mood swings – you want them to have sufficient self-esteem to become a contributing adult – but a frisson of uncertainty will keep them on their toes. Rewarding good behaviour with a dry Weetabix nine times out of ten sets the standard, an occasional extra treat of an unexpected marmite topping will encourage them to go that extra mile.

* ### Punishment

  In my experience parents tend to be overly timid in

their punishments. I thoroughly encourage what I call 'safe scaring', i.e. where the child may be mildly scared, purely for sound behavioural aims, but you know it is done in a completely safe environment. For example, one toddler in my care scribbled crayons on the table, so as punishment I gave him what he thought was a tattoo of a pink, girly fairy on his cheek. Of course it wasn't done with a real tattoo needle! I merely did it with a permanent marker, which I knew would wash out after a couple of months. He was genuinely upset for about six weeks so the message got across. The corollary benefits were that I was able to reinforce the value of cleanliness *and* the superiority of his elders and betters. The tragic footnote to this story is that his mother simply didn't have the intelligence to understand my approach. I think the upcoming court case says more about her than it does about me. All donations to the legal fighting fund are gratefully received.

Embrace the opportunity to be creative with your punishments. Turn the negative episode into a benefit or a powerful learning experience. My personal favourite is the 'naughty potato'. Get your errant child to hold a potato for a few minutes. In contrast to the 'naughty step' which creates isolation and resentment (as well as discriminating against families who live in stair-less flats) the naughty potato encourages intrigue and dialogue. 'Why a potato?' ponders the toddler, 'Why do I need to hold it?' and (in later years) 'Is it a King Edwards or a Pink? Why not a Maris Piper?'

Obviously the naughty potato is slightly more challenging with very young babies who can't physically grasp things yet, but most get the message when a random potato is put into their buggy. The odd one doesn't – I know of a child who got quite attached to potatoes in her pram – but really, in the grand scheme of things, where's the harm in that?

Conclusion

Good discipline creates good behaviour and surely that is the essence of good parenting? It is a gift that money and status can't buy, as the following story illustrates:

I holidayed with a celebrity client recently. I often find these poor souls are the ones most needing my help. Whereas many of the lower classes have a natural aptitude for breeding (which must have something to do with their vital historical role in creating the manpower for the cotton mills) and the upper classes have a tried and tested system of nannies and public schools to rely on, the noveaux-riche fall horribly between two stools. They end up calling their children names which would be more suitable for cheap cocktails and encourage them to vlog rather than learn their times tables.

When I arrived at the villa I found three year-old Sherry Mistletoe and his one year old sister Orgasma

Petunia running round the pool shouting 'mummy is a poo-head' and throwing raisins at the chauffeur. Within five minutes I had made sure both children had clean hands, were wearing starched linen and were holding a 'naughty mango' (I am a flexible professional). In the ensuing days the children helped the chauffeur to strip down and recondition the limousine's engine, thereby not only making amends for their shameful raisin-throwing, but learning valuable life skills – indeed they were well on their way to an automotive mechanical NVQ by the end of the holiday. It is regrettable in the extreme that the parents misinterpreted this as child labour.

Although I cannot comment on ongoing legal proceedings I can confirm that yes I did have a romantic liaison with the Juan chauffeur and this in no way affected my professional judgement. I also fully acknowledge that the children earned money at Juan's garage helping him with other clients but I am profoundly offended at the parents' suspicions that I *took* this money. I was merely looking after it for them. It is also true that I was actually employed to look after the family's cat on that holiday rather than their children, but I struggle when duty calls one has to step in. To call it 'Overstepping the terms of employment' and to focus needlessly on my lack of formal childcare qualifications is hurtful and wrong. All donations to the legal fighting fund are gratefully received.

A FINAL WORD...

I can't quite believe I'm writing the final pages of this book. It's been a tough journey of sacrifice and effort. I've not hosted bridge club as often as I should and I didn't get to see the exhibition of Victorian bath chairs at the Victoria and Albert Museum that I was so keen to. But I truly believe it's a price worth paying. To think that I may have helped even just a few parents and guardians tread the right path has kept me going.

When you are recommending this, dare I say it, life changing manual to friends and family, please don't refer to it as taking you on 'a journey'. A journey' is a trip from, say, London to Birmingham, or, if you are more fortunate, Birmingham to London. The notion of some form of emotional journey has been so hijacked by the dreadful Simon Cowell and his kind that the original meaning has been lost and I fear the next generation will be unable to leave their sofas, let alone ride a train, without expecting some kind of personality transformation.

But I digress…

If at any time in the ensuing months and years you feel at a loss with regard to how you should parent your growing child, pick up this book or get in touch to make use of the plethora of invaluable products at www.helpfulhumour.com. I would also recommend you look out for my next book: turnip-led schooling. Unfortunately, the Association of Independent schools is giving legal challenge to my Turnip Academy chain, on the ludicrous charge that it 'fails to meet their quality standards'. You know me well enough by now to expect the rigorous defence I am mounting. All donations to the legal fighting fund are, as ever, gratefully received.

About the Author

Harriet Beveridge is a stand up comic, executive coach and a mum of two boys (at the time of writing aged 6 and 8). She was semi-finalist in the Funny Women National Stand Up Awards in 2011 and is taking her show, 'Mummy's gone a bit parental' to the Edinburgh Fringe in August 2015. Follow her @mummysgoneabit on Twitter, find her on Facebook, or get a dose of laughter therapy at www.helpfulhumour.com.